11+
PRACTICE PAPERS

Series editor Tracey Phelps,
the 11+ tutor with a

96% PASS RATE

Maths

English

Verbal Reasoning

Non-verbal Reasoning

Ages 9–10

Practice

SCHOLASTIC

Published in the UK by Scholastic, 2020

Book End, Range Road, Witney, Oxfordshire, OX29 0YD

Scholastic Ireland, 89E Lagan Road, Dublin Industrial Estate, Glasnevin, Dublin, D11 HP5F

SCHOLASTIC and associated logos are trademarks and/or registered trademarks of Scholastic Inc.

www.scholastic.co.uk

1 2 3 4 5 6 7 8 9   1 2 3 4 5 6 7 8 9 0

A CIP catalogue record for this book is available from the British Library.

ISBN 978-1407-18372-5

Printed and bound by Replika Press Pvt. Ltd.

Paper made from wood grown in sustainable forests and other controlled sources.

Every effort has been made to trace copyright holders for the works reproduced in this publication, and the publishers apologise for any inadvertent omissions.

Author

Tracey Phelps

Editorial team

Rachel Morgan, Suzanne Holloway, Audrey Stokes, Sarah Davies, Mandy Ridd

Design team

Dipa Mistry

Illustrations

Tracey Phelps

Acknowledgements

p13: The Riddle of the Frozen Flame; p16: Poems of the Sea; p61: The Young King; p62: Coral Island (c) Scholastic Ltd

p62: Extract adapted from *The Secret Garden* by Frances Hodgson Burnett © Scholastic

Contents

About the CEM test

About the CEM test

The Centre for Evaluation and Monitoring (CEM) is one of the leading providers of the tests that grammar schools use in selecting students at 11+. The CEM test assesses a student's ability in Verbal Reasoning, Non-verbal Reasoning, English and Mathematics. Pupils typically take the CEM test at the start of Year 6.

Students answer multiple-choice questions and record their answers on a separate answer sheet. This answer sheet is then marked via OMR (Optical Mark Recognition) scanning technology.

The content and question type may vary slightly each year. The English and Verbal Reasoning components have included synonyms, antonyms, word associations, shuffled sentences, cloze (gap fill) passages and comprehension questions.

The Mathematics and Non-verbal Reasoning components span the Key Stage 2 Mathematics curriculum, with emphasis on worded problems. It is useful to note that the CEM test may include Mathematics topics which students will be introduced to in Year 6, such as ratio, proportion and probability.

The other main provider of such tests is GL Assessment. The GLA test assesses the same subjects as the CEM test and uses a multiple-choice format.

About this book

Scholastic 11+ Practice Papers for the CEM Test Ages 9–10 is part of the Pass Your 11+ series. The practice papers in this book have been designed to accurately reflect the format and style of the CEM test. The CEM test consists of two question papers, each of which contains elements of the four subjects being tested. Each test paper is divided into four or five sections with strict timings for each section. Students are not permitted to move backwards or forwards between the different sections during the test.

This book offers:

- Two full-length CEM-style papers to familiarise your child with the CEM test.
- Timings for each section to help your child become accustomed to working under time pressure.
- Multiple-choice questions to practise answering the types of question your child will meet in their CEM test.
- Multiple-choice answer sheets.
- Answers.
- Visit **https://shop.scholastic.co.uk/pass-your-11-plus/extras** for extended answers and additional answer sheets.

CEM-style 11+ Mixed Assessment Practice Paper A

Information about this practice paper:

- The time allowed is given at the start of each section.

- The page number appears at the bottom of each page.

- The title of each section is provided on the top line of each page.

- Answers should be clearly marked in pencil on the answer sheets on pages 38 and 39, in the spaces provided. Additional answer sheets are available at **https://shop.scholastic.co.uk/pass-your-11-plus/extras.**

- Use the pages of the test to write your workings out.

- If you make a mistake, rub it out and insert your new answer.

- If you are not sure of an answer, choose the one you think would be best; do not leave it blank.

 You will see this symbol at the beginning of each section. It will tell you how many minutes are allowed for that section.

Blank page

Synonyms

Instructions

Select the word that has the SAME or SIMILAR meaning to the word on the left.
Mark your answer on the answer sheet (page 38) by choosing one of the options A–E.
There is only one correct answer for each question.

Example 1

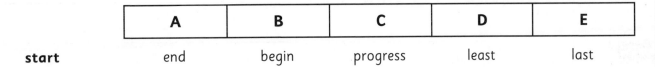

A	B	C	D	E
end	begin	progress	least	last

start

The correct answer is: | **B** |

begin

The answer, B, has been marked for you on the answer sheet.

Example 2

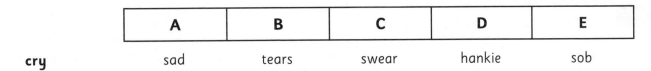

A	B	C	D	E
sad	tears	swear	hankie	sob

cry

The correct answer is: | **E** |

sob

Mark the box with the letter E on the answer sheet.

 You have 5 minutes for this section.

1

show

A	B	C	D	E
excavation	examination	(exhibition)	expedition	exploration

2

outwit

A	B	C	D	E
outbid	outdate	(outsmart)	outjump	outstay

3

overcast

A	B	C	D	E
(cloudy)	muddy	mushy	foggy	dusky

4

late

A	B	C	D	E
unpaid	(overdue)	open	postponed	punctual

5

deal

A	B	C	D	E
argument	achievement	adjustment	appointment	(agreement)

6

unsatisfactory

A	B	C	D	E
unmistakable	(unavailable)	unsociable	unacceptable	undeniable

7

tolerant

A	B	C	D	E
potent	tender	(tough)	pleasant	patient

8		A	B	C	D	E
pause		disagree	(discontinue)	discourage	disallow	disguise

9		A	B	C	D	E
punishment		goal	kick	(penalty)	throw	corner

10		A	B	C	D	E
unfaithful		(disloyal)	deceitful	artful	devious	shrewd

11		A	B	C	D	E
perplex		dazzle	frizzle	muzzle	sizzle	(puzzle)

12		A	B	C	D	E
harass		teach	(torment)	trust	(thrive)	trample

13		A	B	C	D	E
fear		trivia	phase	phobia	fable	fiasco

14		A	B	C	D	E
hazard		(danger)	misery	scorn	mockery	nuisance

15

calm

A	B	C	D	E
seethe	(soothe)	sense	salute	stroke

16

competitor

A	B	C	D	E
convict	comrade	(contestant)	carpenter	chairman

17

pleased

A	B	C	D	E
canny	charitable	corrupt	(contented)	comfortable

18

toxic

A	B	C	D	E
(venomous)	enormous	infamous	anonymous	basic

19

swoop

A	B	C	D	E
spring	shoot	dwindle	fade	plummet

20

suppose

A	B	C	D	E
overlook	suspect	omit	assume	trust

21

habit

A	B	C	D	E
function	custom	design	method	scheme

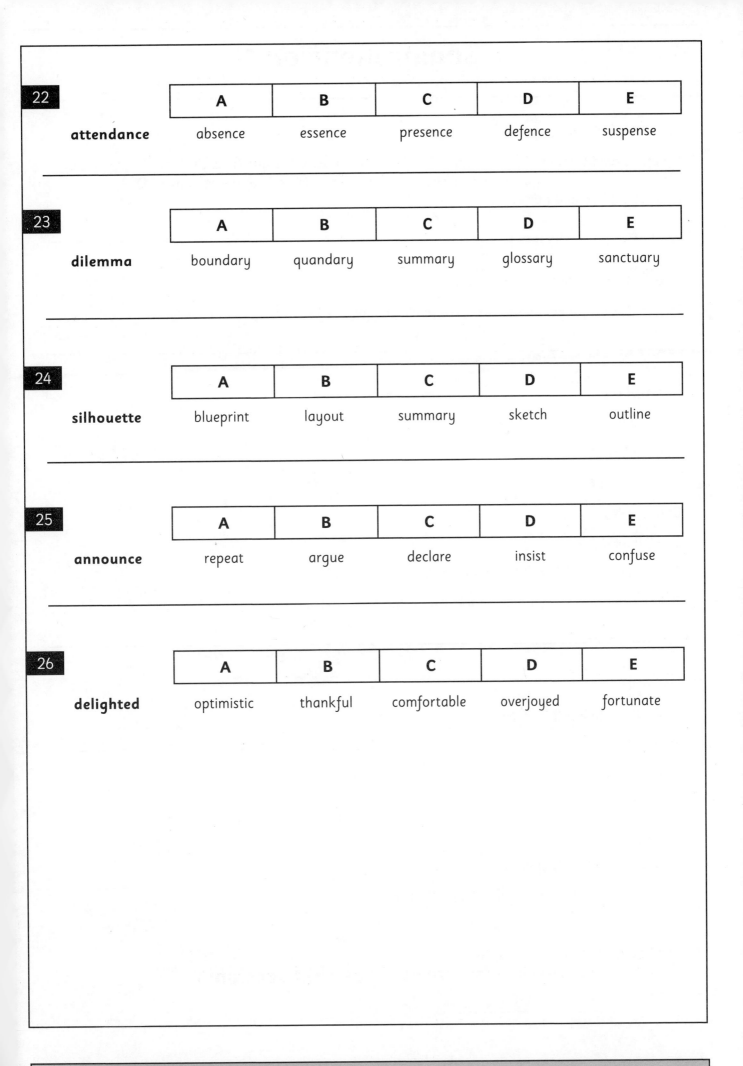

22

A	B	C	D	E

attendance absence essence presence defence suspense

23

A	B	C	D	E

dilemma boundary quandary summary glossary sanctuary

24

A	B	C	D	E

silhouette blueprint layout summary sketch outline

25

A	B	C	D	E

announce repeat argue declare insist confuse

26

A	B	C	D	E

delighted optimistic thankful comfortable overjoyed fortunate

Comprehension 1

Instructions

Carefully read through the passages of writing. Then answer the questions that follow. Mark your answer on the answer sheet (page 38) by choosing one of the options A–D. Look at the examples below.

Example passage

The boys went fishing by the river. They only caught one fish.

Example 1

Where did the boys go fishing?

A. By the river

B. In the pond

C. In the sea

D. By the lake

The correct answer is A, 'By the river'.

The answer, A, has been marked for you on the answer sheet.

Example 2

How many fish did they catch?

A. Fifteen

B. None

C. Plenty

D. One

The correct answer is D, 'One'.

Mark the box with letter D on the answer sheet.

 You have **14** minutes for this section.

The Riddle of the Frozen Flame

A novel from the Inspector Cleek *mystery series, first published in 1920, features gold robberies, jealousy, murder and mysterious flames that appear in marshy meadows in the dead of night. At this point in the story, Nigel Merriton has returned to his family home in a remote part of England. During his first night there, Nigel cannot sleep, and notices something surprising from his bedroom window.*

5 Merriton Towers had been called the loneliest spot in England by many of the tourists who visited, and it was not a misnomer. It was a handsome place, no doubt, in its gaunt, grey, prison-like way.

The first night, Nigel hardly slept a wink. His bed was a huge four-poster, circled by plush hangings that closed around him; it creaked at every turn he made, until finally he got up, taking a quilt with him, and spent the rest of the hours upon a sofa beside an open window.

10 "How can people live in such places?" he muttered to himself, over and over again. "No wonder my poor old uncle disappeared!"

He settled himself back against the hard, horsehair sofa and pulled up the blind, instantly filling the room with grey and lavender shadows; outside, the marshes stretched out in unbroken lines into the distance. Merriton lay with his eyes upon the window and surveyed the scene before him with despairing eyes. Not a sign of habitation anywhere – 15 not a vestige of it.

Focusing on the clump of trees that stood out against the semi-darkness of the approaching dawn, he saw a sudden burst of light, like a tiny flame, low down upon the very edge of the Fens. One light, two, three, and then a very host of them flashed out. Instinctively, he got to his feet. What on earth – ? But, even as his lips formed the unspoken exclamation, another light joined the others – dancing, twinkling and flickering out there across the gloomy 20 marshlands. Merriton forced open another window with some effort and gazed at the lights.

In a moment, sleep had gone from his eyelids and he felt thoroughly awake. He must throw on some clothes and investigate, for this was so strange, so incredible. He knew, well enough, that that part of the marshes was uninhabited.

Hastily, he began to dress. As he struggled into a pair of trousers, there was a soft knock on his door. He whipped 25 around as though he had been shot, his nerves shaking from the very atmosphere of the place.

"And who on earth are you?" he snapped.

The door swung open a trifle and the pale face of Borkins, the butler, appeared, his eyes wide with fright and his mouth hanging open. "Sir Nigel, sorry, I 'eard a dreadful noise – like a pistol shot it was, comin' from this room! Anythink the matter, sir?"

30 "Nothing!" broke out Merriton. "The noise you heard was that window, which possibly hasn't been opened for a century or two, groaning in pain at being forced into action again. Can't sleep in this beastly room and then I saw out the window those flames flickering across the horizon.

I've been watching them for the past twenty minutes and they've got on my nerves, so I'm going out to investigate."

Borkins gave a little exclamation of alarm and put one trembling hand over his face. "Please, sir, don't!" he 35 murmured in a shaken voice. "Those lights, sir – if you knew the story! If you values your life at any price at all don't go out, sir, and investigate them."

"What's that?" Merriton swung round and looked into the weak, rather watery, blue eyes of his butler. "What on earth do you mean, Borkins? Why shouldn't I go out and investigate them? Who's to stop me?"

40 "The story's common knowledge, Sir Nigel, sir. Them there flames are strange. Frozen flames the villagers calls 'em, because they don't seem to give out no 'eat. Nobody lives in that part of the Fens and there isn't a single person in the whole village that would venture anywhere near it after dark."

"Why?"

"Because they never comes back, that's why, sir!" said Borkins. "'Tisn't an old wives' tale neither—there's been cases by the score. Only a matter of six months ago, one of the boys from the mill said he was a-goin'
45 ter see who it was wot made them flames light up by theirselves, but he never came back, and a new flame appeared the next night."

"Whew! Bit of a tall story, Borkins!" Nevertheless, a cold chill crept over Merriton's bones and he gave a forced, mirthless laugh. "You've fairly made my flesh creep with your beastly story!" he said, in a rather high-pitched voice.

Adapted from a novel by Thomas W. Hanshew and Mary E. Hanshew

---

1 What were the underfoot conditions like in the Fens?

A. The ground was gravelly and coarse.

B. It was sodden and swampy.

C. The conditions were frosty and crisp.

D. The ground was lush and verdant.

---

2 For how long did Merriton assert that a window in his room had remained closed?

A. For possibly up to 200 years

B. For a decade

C. For at least several months

D. Since the previous summer

---

3 Which two adjectives best describe Borkins when he first enters his master's room?

A. Chatty but nervous

B. Grumpy and rude

C. Serious and shy

D. Wide-eyed and ashen-faced

---

4 What relation was Nigel Merriton to the man who had disappeared in the Fens?

A. He was his uncle.

B. They were brothers.

C. He was his nephew.

D. He was his son.

---

5 Which one of the adjectives below is mentioned when describing Merriton's bed?

A. Hard

B. Huge

C. Comfortable

D. Soft

---

6 According to the text, which events do not feature in *The Riddle of the Frozen Flame*?

A. Burglaries

B. Acts of envy

C. Romance

D. Killing

---

7 What time of day did Merriton first notice the flames in the Fens?

A. Just before midnight

B. Five minutes past midnight

C. Dusk

D. Just before daybreak

Comprehension 2

The Sea

THE SEA, the sea, the open sea!
The blue, the fresh, the ever free!
Without a mark, without a bound,
It runs the earth's wide girth around,
It plays with clouds, it mocks the skies,
Or like a cradled creature lies.

I'm on the sea! I'm on the sea!
I'm where I'll always long to be,
With the blue above, and the blue below,
And silence everywhere I go,
If storms should come and stir the deep,
It matters not – I'll ride and sleep.

Whenever I'm on the dull, tame shore,
I love the sea yet more and more,
So back I fly to the place that's best,
Like a bird that seeks its home – the nest,
And like a home the sea is to me,
For I was born on the open sea!

The waves were white, and red the morn,
In the noisy hour when I was born,
And the whale it whistled, the porpoise rolled,
And the dolphins bared their backs of gold,
And never was heard such an outcry wild,
When the sea rose to welcome the ocean-child!

I've lived since then, in calm and strife,
A full fifty summers, a sailor's life,
With wealth to spend and adventures of range,
Never have I been short of change,
And Death, whenever he comes to me,
Shall come on the wild, unbounded sea!

Written by Barry Cornwall

1 How old is the main character in the poem?

A. 40 years old

B. 50 years old

C. 30 years old

D. 20 years old

---

2 What is meant in line 4 of the first stanza?

A. The sea flows right to the centre of the earth.

B. The sea goes down to the bottom of the earth.

C. The sea runs dry at the centre of the earth.

D. The sea swirls right around the circumference of the earth.

---

3 Which line of the poem contains an example of alliteration?

A. 'It runs the earth's wide girth around'

B. 'So back I fly to the place that's best'

C. 'And the whale it whistled, the porpoise rolled'

D. 'And like a home the sea is to me'

---

4 What does the author mean in the following lines of the poem:

'So back I fly to the place that's best,
Like a bird that seeks its home – the nest'

A. He feels at his happiest on the sea and wishes to return.

B. He needs to be with his mother again.

C. He wishes to be on land in a bird's nest.

D. He wants to swim with the dolphins.

Blank page

Pictures 1

Instructions

There is a set of pictures on the left with a missing picture shown by a question mark. Choose one of the pictures from the right to complete the set. Mark your answer on the answer sheet (page 38) by choosing one of the options A–F. Look at the examples below.

Example 1

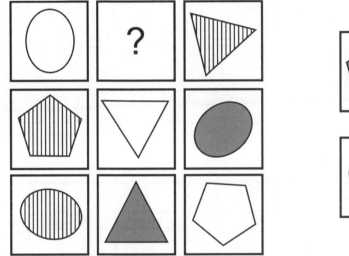 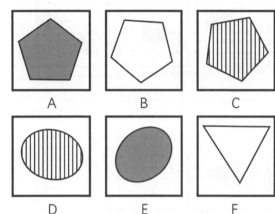

The answer to example 1 is A.

The answer, A, has been marked for you on the answer sheet.

Example 2

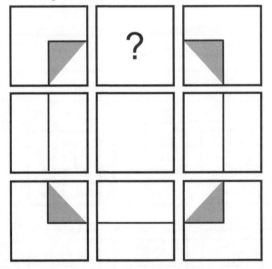 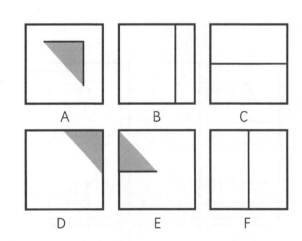

The answer to example 2 is C.

Mark the box with the letter C on the answer sheet.

 You have 9 minutes for this section.

1

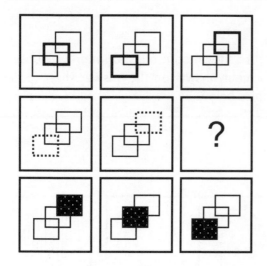

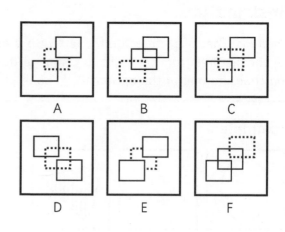

A	B	C
D	E	F

2

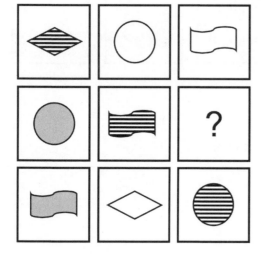

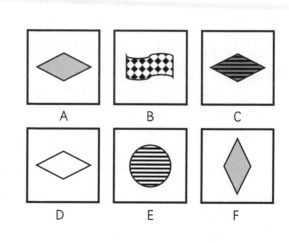

A	B	C
D	E	F

3

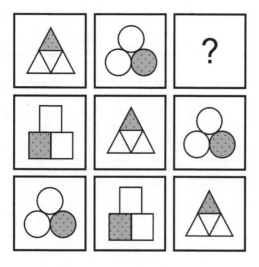

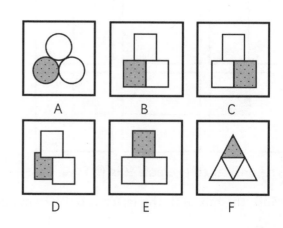

A	B	C
D	E	F

4

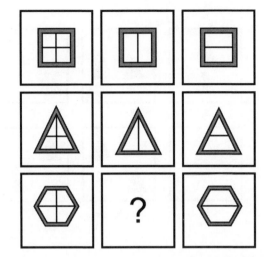

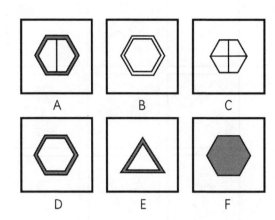

5

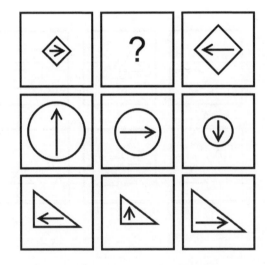

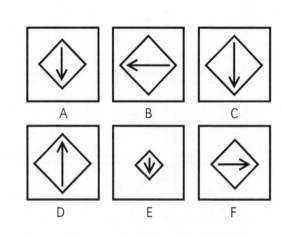

6

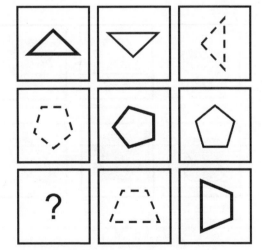

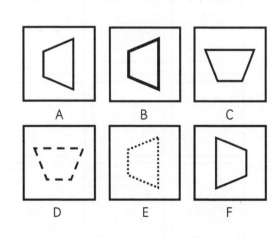

7

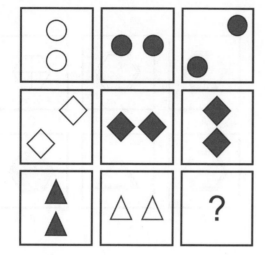
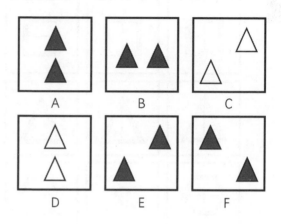

8

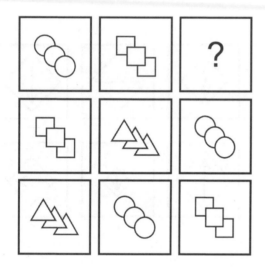
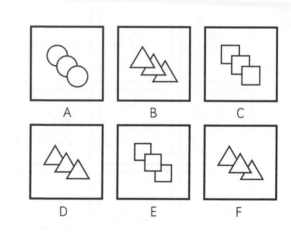

9

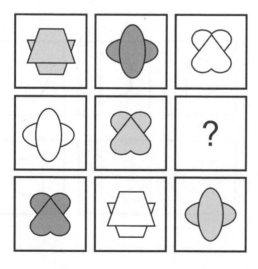
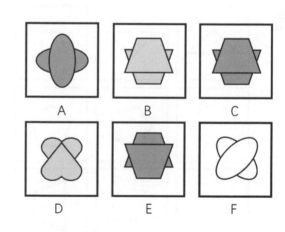

10

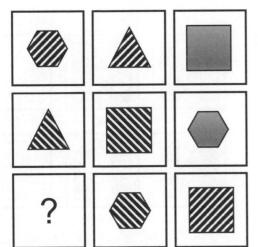

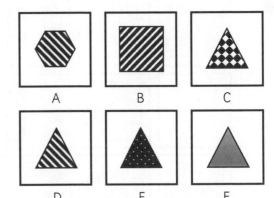

11

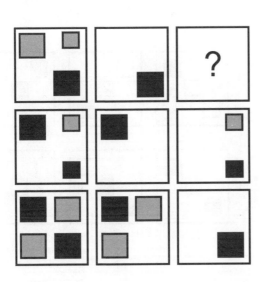

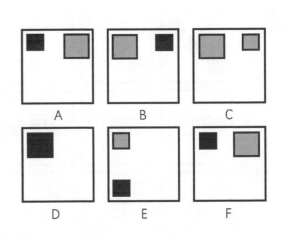

12

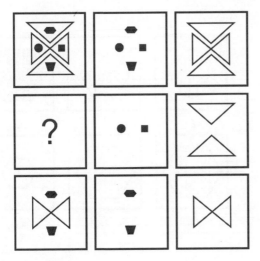

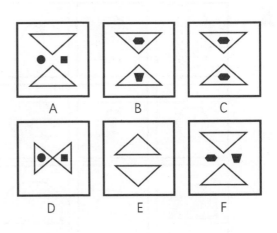

13

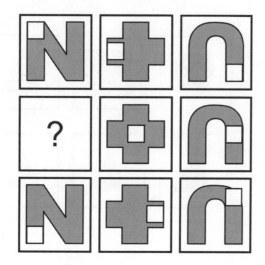 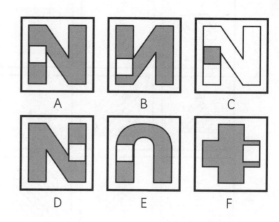

14

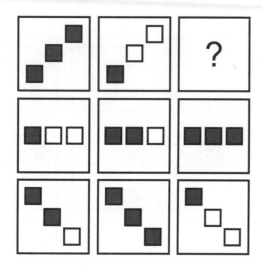 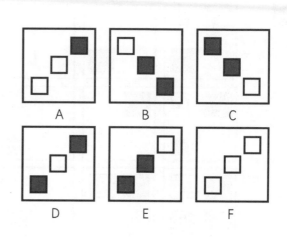

15

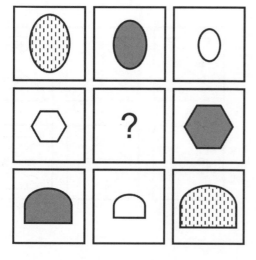 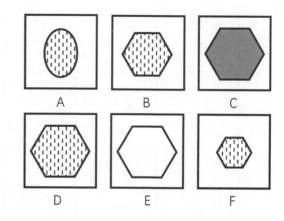

16

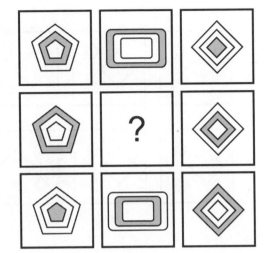

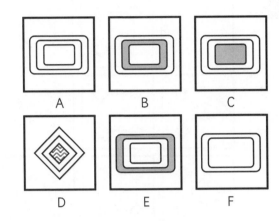

17

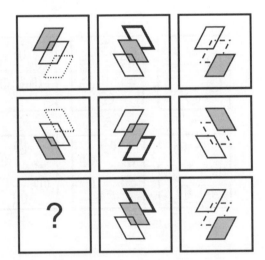

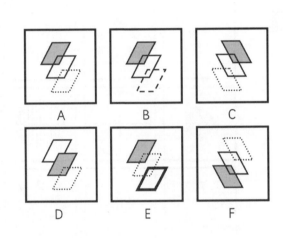

18

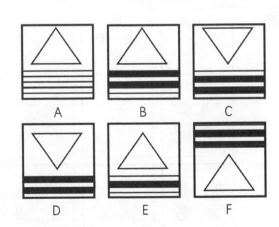

19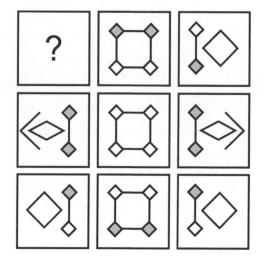

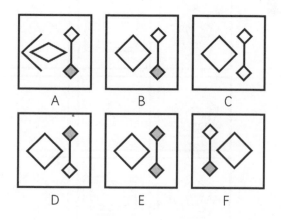

20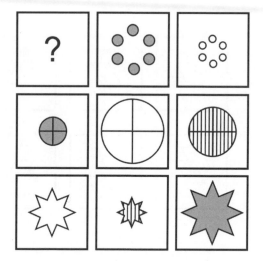

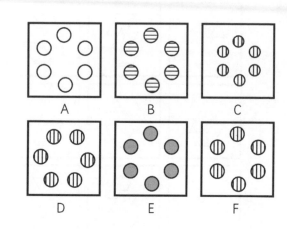

21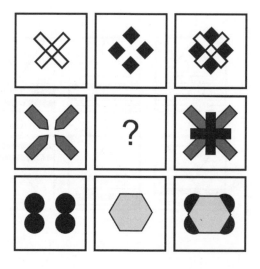

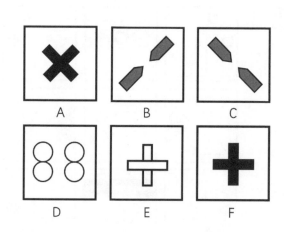

Maths 1

Instructions

In this section, choose one option from A–E to answer the question.

Mark your answer on the answer sheet (page 39) by choosing one of the options A–E.

Look at the examples below.

Example 1

What is 14 + 38?

A	B	C	D	E
54	52	62	64	48

The answer is:

B
52

The answer, B, has been marked for you on the answer sheet.

Example 2

Which of the following numbers is a squared number greater than 64 and smaller than 100?

A	B	C	D	E
121	49	144	81	100

The answer is:

D
81

Mark the box with the letter D on the answer sheet.

 You have 12 minutes for this section.

---

1 A tin of baked beans weighs 400g. Roberta heats up three tins and spoons the beans out equally on to six plates. How many grams of baked beans will there be on each plate?

A	B	C	D	E
200g	150g	175g	225g	250g

2 Simon was late for school one morning and had to run all the way to the bus stop. He arrived at the bus stop at 08:07 and realised that he had missed the bus by 11 minutes.

At what time did the bus depart from the bus stop?

A	B	C	D	E
07:59	08:18	08:03	07:56	07:55

3 Five portions of fish and chips cost £39.75.

What would be the cost of two portions of fish and chips?

A	B	C	D	E
£14.95	£7.95	£15.90	£22.15	£16.90

4 A helicopter is en route to rescue some stranded mountain climbers. It turns 90° clockwise in order to proceed on a northerly course.

In which direction was the helicopter flying before it changed its course?

A	B	C	D	E
south-east	west	south	east	north

5   Nathan and Bartek share a pizza. Bartek eats one third of the pizza and Nathan eats one half of the remaining pizza. What fraction of the pizza remains?

A	B	C	D	E
$\frac{4}{5}$	$\frac{1}{4}$	$\frac{1}{5}$	$\frac{1}{8}$	$\frac{1}{3}$

6   At 09:20, Lydia boards a coach travelling from London to Bristol. The journey takes 2 hours and 40 minutes. She has to wait ten minutes before boarding another coach to Exeter, where she arrives safely at 14:10.

How long did Lydia's second coach journey last?

A	B	C	D	E
1 hr 20 mins	1 hr 40 mins	2 hrs 10 mins	1 hr 50 mins	2 hours

7   At midnight in Edinburgh, the temperature is −2°C. The temperature continues to fall by 1°C every hour until 06:00 when it begins to rise.

What will be the temperature at 04:00?

A	B	C	D	E
−5°C	−4°C	−7°C	−6°C	−3°C

8   Jim sees a new car in a showroom priced at £17,500. The following week, he notices that the price for the same car has been reduced by £3500.

By what percentage has the car been reduced?

A	B	C	D	E
25%	32.5%	20%	15%	17.5%

9 Layla has £3670 in her savings account and her brother Syed has £452 more in his savings account. They are trying save a total of £12,000 between them.

How much more do they need to save to reach their target?

A	B	C	D	E
£4118	£4208	£5208	£4908	£4108

10 If 20% of an amount of money equals £25, what is the total sum of money?

A	B	C	D	E
£100	£130	£150	£125	£115

11 Saskia weighs out 120g of sugar for a cake recipe. This is 20% more than she actually needs.

How much flour should she have weighed out?

A	B	C	D	E
100g	140g	80g	75g	90g

12 If the last day of August falls on a Friday, on which day of the week will 8 September fall?

A	B	C	D	E
Sunday	Monday	Saturday	Friday	Thursday

13 The current population of the city of Bristol is 525,948.

What is this number rounded to the nearest one hundred?

A	B	C	D	E
525,000	526,000	525,800	525,500	525,900

14 Stella puts a chicken in the oven at 12:45 to cook for 2 hours and 45 minutes.

What time will she need to remove the chicken from the oven?

A	B	C	D	E
15:10	15:20	16:30	15:30	14:30

15 Two coaches are booked for a school outing to Brighton. The first coach seats 65 passengers and the second coach seats 32. Six teachers, 30 boys and 42 girls will be going on the trip.

How many spare passenger seats will there be?

A	B	C	D	E
11	19	5	8	4

16 How many degrees will there be in the obtuse angle between the hour and the minute hand on a clock when the time is exactly 4.00pm?

A	B	C	D	E
120°	125°	140°	110°	115°

17 Six children shared the first prize money in a poetry writing competition.

They each received £125.

What was the total money offered as the first prize?

A	B	C	D	E
£500	£525	£725	£700	£750

18 There are 42 passenger seats on Elliot's school bus and one morning there are 45 children on the bus. Three children have to stand.

What is the probability that Elliot has to stand?

A	B	C	D	E
1 in 12	1 in 14	1 in 15	1 in 18	1 in 20

19 Ajay visits a cafe for his lunch. He buys a packet of crisps, a sandwich and a coffee. The sandwich and the coffee cost exactly the same amount as each other and the crisps are half the price of the sandwich. His bill comes to £7.50.

How much are the crisps?

A	B	C	D	E
£1.25	90p	£2.25	£1.50	£1.70

20 If I have four different British coins, what is the most amount of money I could have?

A	B	C	D	E
£4.00	£3.70	£8.00	£4.50	£2.70

21 An empty milk crate weighs 1.2kg. The crate is filled with 12 identical milk bottles and now weighs 4.8kg.

How much does one bottle of milk weigh?

A	B	C	D	E
300g	250g	270g	350g	325g

Maths 2

Instructions

In this section, mark your answer on the answer sheet (page 39) by filling in the correct number. Look at the examples below.

Example 1

What is 18 minus 12?

The answer is 6 and has been marked for you on the answer sheet.

The number 6 is written as '06' in the top boxes and the corresponding

digits '0' and '6' are marked in the boxes below.

0	6
[0̶]	[0]
[1]	[1]
[2]	[2]
[3]	[3]
[4]	[4]
[5]	[5]
[6]	[6̶]
[7]	[7]
[8]	[8]
[9]	[9]

Example 2

What is 18 × 4?

The answer is 72.

Mark the correct answer 72 on the answer sheet.

 You have **10** minutes for this section.

1 How many of the smaller shampoo bottles will hold the same amount of shampoo as one large shampoo bottle?

600ml   120ml

---

2 Joe is driving from Bristol to Manchester, a distance of 168 miles. After he has been driving for 2 hours and 20 minutes, he has travelled exactly two thirds of the distance.

How many more miles does Joe still have to drive?

---

3 Amalia and Lily play for the same football team. At the end of the season they have scored a total of 64 goals between them. Amalia has scored 14 more goals than Lily.

How many goals has Lily scored?

---

4 Mr Jessop, the school caretaker, is carrying boxes of paper upstairs. He can manage three boxes on each trip and he has a total of 37 boxes to take upstairs.

How many trips upstairs must he take before all the boxes are where they are needed?

5 All the ages in the Lomax family add up to 108.

Brian is two years older than Sue, who is 40 years old.

The eldest daughter, Sasha, is twice as old as Annie – the youngest of their three children.

Their middle child, Millie, is two years older than Annie.

How old is Sasha?

---

6 Ahmed would like to buy a used car priced at £2000.

The seller offers Ahmed a discount of 20% if he can pay for the car in cash.

Ahmed agrees and withdraws the exact amount needed in £20 notes.

How many £20 notes does Ahmed withdraw from his bank?

---

7 There are two layers of chocolates in a box.

Each layer contains 20 chocolates.

20% of the chocolates are milk chocolate and the rest are dark chocolates.

How many of the chocolates are dark chocolates?

8 There are 56 floors in the hotel that Bobby is staying at on his holiday.

Bobby's room is on the 12th floor.

How many floors is Bobby's room from the top floor of the hotel?

9 In St James's Primary School there are 90 students in Year 5.

Three fifths of the pupils are boys.

How many girls are there in Year 5 at St James's?

10 Mrs Holt buys ten boxes of doughnuts for the last day of term.

Each box contains six doughnuts and she has 28 children in her class.

Each child helps themselves to two doughnuts and she eats one doughnut herself.

How many doughnuts are left over?

11 Yasmin is having a trampolining party for her tenth birthday.

The cost for each child is £15.

Her parents have set a budget of £200 for the event and they don't have to pay for Yasmin.

What is the maximum number of friends that Yasmin may invite to her party?

---

12 In a survey, 156 people were asked if they liked yoghurt.

Three quarters of those surveyed answered 'yes'.

How many did not like yoghurt?

Answer sheets

Student name:

Synonyms p.7

Examples:

1   [A]   [B]   [C]   [D]   [E]
2   [A]   [B]   [C]   [D]   [E]

Questions

1   [A]   [B]   [C]   [D]   [E]
2   [A]   [B]   [C]   [D]   [E]
3   [A]   [B]   [C]   [D]   [E]
4   [A]   [B]   [C]   [D]   [E]
5   [A]   [B]   [C]   [D]   [E]
6   [A]   [B]   [C]   [D]   [E]
7   [A]   [B]   [C]   [D]   [E]
8   [A]   [B]   [C]   [D]   [E]
9   [A]   [B]   [C]   [D]   [E]
10   [A]   [B]   [C]   [D]   [E]
11   [A]   [B]   [C]   [D]   [E]
12   [A]   [B]   [C]   [D]   [E]
13   [A]   [B]   [C]   [D]   [E]
14   [A]   [B]   [C]   [D]   [E]
15   [A]   [B]   [C]   [D]   [E]
16   [A]   [B]   [C]   [D]   [E]
17   [A]   [B]   [C]   [D]   [E]
18   [A]   [B]   [C]   [D]   [E]
19   [A]   [B]   [C]   [D]   [E]
20   [A]   [B]   [C]   [D]   [E]
21   [A]   [B]   [C]   [D]   [E]
22   [A]   [B]   [C]   [D]   [E]
23   [A]   [B]   [C]   [D]   [E]
24   [A]   [B]   [C]   [D]   [E]
25   [A]   [B]   [C]   [D]   [E]
26   [A]   [B]   [C]   [D]   [E]

Comprehension 1 p.12

Examples:

1   [A]   [B]   [C]   [D]
2   [A]   [B]   [C]   [D]

Questions

1   [A]   [B]   [C]   [D]
2   [A]   [B]   [C]   [D]
3   [A]   [B]   [C]   [D]
4   [A]   [B]   [C]   [D]
5   [A]   [B]   [C]   [D]
6   [A]   [B]   [C]   [D]
7   [A]   [B]   [C]   [D]

Comprehension 2 p.16

Questions

1   [A]   [B]   [C]   [D]
2   [A]   [B]   [C]   [D]
3   [A]   [B]   [C]   [D]
4   [A]   [B]   [C]   [D]

Pictures 1 p.19

Examples:

1   [A]   [B]   [C]   [D]   [E]   [F]
2   [A]   [B]   [C]   [D]   [E]   [F]

Questions

1   [A]   [B]   [C]   [D]   [E]   [F]
2   [A]   [B]   [C]   [D]   [E]   [F]
3   [A]   [B]   [C]   [D]   [E]   [F]
4   [A]   [B]   [C]   [D]   [E]   [F]
5   [A]   [B]   [C]   [D]   [E]   [F]
6   [A]   [B]   [C]   [D]   [E]   [F]
7   [A]   [B]   [C]   [D]   [E]   [F]
8   [A]   [B]   [C]   [D]   [E]   [F]
9   [A]   [B]   [C]   [D]   [E]   [F]
10   [A]   [B]   [C]   [D]   [E]   [F]
11   [A]   [B]   [C]   [D]   [E]   [F]
12   [A]   [B]   [C]   [D]   [E]   [F]
13   [A]   [B]   [C]   [D]   [E]   [F]
14   [A]   [B]   [C]   [D]   [E]   [F]
15   [A]   [B]   [C]   [D]   [E]   [F]
16   [A]   [B]   [C]   [D]   [E]   [F]
17   [A]   [B]   [C]   [D]   [E]   [F]
18   [A]   [B]   [C]   [D]   [E]   [F]
19   [A]   [B]   [C]   [D]   [E]   [F]
20   [A]   [B]   [C]   [D]   [E]   [F]
21   [A]   [B]   [C]   [D]   [E]   [F]

Maths 1 p.27

Examples:

1	[A]	~~[B]~~	[C]	[D]	[E]
2	[A]	[B]	[C]	[D]	[E]

Questions

1	[A]	[B]	[C]	[D]	[E]
2	[A]	[B]	[C]	[D]	[E]
3	[A]	[B]	[C]	[D]	[E]
4	[A]	[B]	[C]	[D]	[E]
5	[A]	[B]	[C]	[D]	[E]
6	[A]	[B]	[C]	[D]	[E]
7	[A]	[B]	[C]	[D]	[E]
8	[A]	[B]	[C]	[D]	[E]
9	[A]	[B]	[C]	[D]	[E]
10	[A]	[B]	[C]	[D]	[E]
11	[A]	[B]	[C]	[D]	[E]
12	[A]	[B]	[C]	[D]	[E]
13	[A]	[B]	[C]	[D]	[E]
14	[A]	[B]	[C]	[D]	[E]
15	[A]	[B]	[C]	[D]	[E]
16	[A]	[B]	[C]	[D]	[E]
17	[A]	[B]	[C]	[D]	[E]
18	[A]	[B]	[C]	[D]	[E]
19	[A]	[B]	[C]	[D]	[E]
20	[A]	[B]	[C]	[D]	[E]
21	[A]	[B]	[C]	[D]	[E]

Maths 2 p.33

Examples:

1

0	6
~~[0]~~	[0]
[1]	[1]
[2]	[2]
[3]	[3]
[4]	[4]
[5]	[5]
[6]	~~[6]~~
[7]	[7]
[8]	[8]
[9]	[9]

2

[0]	[0]
[1]	[1]
[2]	[2]
[3]	[3]
[4]	[4]
[5]	[5]
[6]	[6]
[7]	[7]
[8]	[8]
[9]	[9]

Questions

1

[0]	[0]
[1]	[1]
[2]	[2]
[3]	[3]
[4]	[4]
[5]	[5]
[6]	[6]
[7]	[7]
[8]	[8]
[9]	[9]

4

[0]	[0]
[1]	[1]
[2]	[2]
[3]	[3]
[4]	[4]
[5]	[5]
[6]	[6]
[7]	[7]
[8]	[8]
[9]	[9]

7

[0]	[0]
[1]	[1]
[2]	[2]
[3]	[3]
[4]	[4]
[5]	[5]
[6]	[6]
[7]	[7]
[8]	[8]
[9]	[9]

10

[0]	[0]
[1]	[1]
[2]	[2]
[3]	[3]
[4]	[4]
[5]	[5]
[6]	[6]
[7]	[7]
[8]	[8]
[9]	[9]

2

[0]	[0]
[1]	[1]
[2]	[2]
[3]	[3]
[4]	[4]
[5]	[5]
[6]	[6]
[7]	[7]
[8]	[8]
[9]	[9]

5

[0]	[0]
[1]	[1]
[2]	[2]
[3]	[3]
[4]	[4]
[5]	[5]
[6]	[6]
[7]	[7]
[8]	[8]
[9]	[9]

8

[0]	[0]
[1]	[1]
[2]	[2]
[3]	[3]
[4]	[4]
[5]	[5]
[6]	[6]
[7]	[7]
[8]	[8]
[9]	[9]

11

[0]	[0]
[1]	[1]
[2]	[2]
[3]	[3]
[4]	[4]
[5]	[5]
[6]	[6]
[7]	[7]
[8]	[8]
[9]	[9]

3

[0]	[0]
[1]	[1]
[2]	[2]
[3]	[3]
[4]	[4]
[5]	[5]
[6]	[6]
[7]	[7]
[8]	[8]
[9]	[9]

6

[0]	[0]
[1]	[1]
[2]	[2]
[3]	[3]
[4]	[4]
[5]	[5]
[6]	[6]
[7]	[7]
[8]	[8]
[9]	[9]

9

[0]	[0]
[1]	[1]
[2]	[2]
[3]	[3]
[4]	[4]
[5]	[5]
[6]	[6]
[7]	[7]
[8]	[8]
[9]	[9]

12

[0]	[0]
[1]	[1]
[2]	[2]
[3]	[3]
[4]	[4]
[5]	[5]
[6]	[6]
[7]	[7]
[8]	[8]
[9]	[9]

Answers

Synonyms p.7

1	C
2	C
3	A
4	B
5	E
6	D
7	E
8	B
9	C
10	A
11	E
12	B
13	C
14	A
15	B
16	C
17	D
18	A
19	E
20	D
21	B
22	C
23	B
24	E
25	C
26	D

Comprehension 1 p.12

1	B
2	A
3	D
4	C
5	B
6	C
7	D

Comprehension 2 p.16

1	B
2	D
3	C
4	A

Pictures 1 p.19

1	C
2	A
3	B
4	A
5	C
6	C
7	E
8	B
9	C
10	F
11	C
12	A
13	A
14	E
15	D
16	C
17	A
18	B
19	B
20	F
21	F

Maths 1 p.27

1	A
2	D
3	C
4	B
5	E
6	E
7	D
8	C
9	B
10	D
11	A
12	C
13	E
14	D
15	B
16	A
17	E
18	C
19	D
20	B
21	A

Maths 2 p.33

1	05
2	56
3	25
4	13
5	12
6	80
7	32
8	44
9	36
10	03
11	13
12	39

Mixed Assessment Practice Paper A

Extended answers
for Mixed Assessment Practice Paper A

Synonyms p.7

1	Both words mean 'a display'.
2	Both words mean 'to get the better of someone'.
3	Both words mean 'covered with clouds'.
4	Both words mean 'occurring after the proper time'.
5	Both words mean 'a business transaction'.
6	Both words mean 'not meeting the proper standard'.
7	Both words mean 'willing to endure'.
8	Both words mean 'to stop'.
9	Both words mean 'discipline for having done something wrong'.
10	Both words mean 'lacking in loyalty'.
11	Both words mean 'to confuse'.
12	Both words mean 'to annoy'.
13	Both words mean 'an anxiety about something'.
14	Both words mean 'risk'.
15	Both words mean 'to relax'.
16	Both words mean 'people taking part in a challenge'.
17	Both words mean 'happy'.
18	Both words mean 'poisonous'.
19	Both words mean 'to descend quickly'.
20	Both words mean 'to believe something'.
21	Both words mean 'a usual thing to do'.
22	Both words mean 'an appearance at an event'.
23	Both words mean 'a difficult choice'.
24	Both words mean 'a general shape of something'.
25	Both words mean 'to make something known in public'.
26	Both words mean 'very pleased'.

Comprehension 1 p.12

1	Line 2 refers to 'marshy meadows'.
2	Lines 30 and 31 state 'The noise you heard was that window, which possibly hasn't been opened for a century or two'.
3	Lines 27 and 28 state 'The door swung open a trifle and the pale face of Borkins, the butler, appeared, his eyes wide with fright and his mouth hanging open.'
4	Lines 10 and 11 state 'No wonder my poor old uncle disappeared!'
5	Lines 7 and 8 state 'His bed was a huge four-poster, circled by plush hangings that closed around him; it creaked at every turn he made'.
6	Lines 1 and 2 state 'features gold robberies, jealousy, murder and mysterious flames that appear in marshy meadows in the dead of night.'
7	Lines 16 and 17 state 'Focusing on the clump of trees that stood out against the semi-darkness of the approaching dawn, he saw a sudden burst of light, like a tiny flame'.

Comprehension 2 p.16

1	In stanza 5, line 2, it states 'A full fifty summers, a sailor's life'
2	In stanza 1, line 4, it states 'It runs the earth's wide girth around' means the sea swirls right around the circumference of the earth.
3	In stanza 4, line 3, 'And the whale it whistled, the porpoise rolled'
4	In stanza 3, lines 2 and 3 imply that the author feels at his happiest on the sea and wishes to return.

Extended answers
for Mixed Assessment Practice Paper A

Pictures 1 p.19

1	All pictures must have 3 identical shapes with 2 shapes having the same outline and the shape with the remaining outline placed in a different position.
2	The grid contains 3 different shapes with 3 different shading, therefore the missing shape must be a diamond shaded grey.
3	The grid contains 3 different shapes all with identical shading, therefore the missing shape is the 3 rectangles with the shaded rectangle on the left.
4	The pictures on the left of the grid contain the inner lines of the two grids to the right added together.
5	The arrows in the centre of the shapes are rotating 90 degrees clockwise as you move left to right along the grid, and there are small, medium and large outer shapes.
6	Three different shapes with three different outlines. In each row, one shape pointing up, one pointing down and the other shape minus 90 degrees anti-clockwise.
7	Two shapes in each square, lined up vertically, horizontally and bottom left corner to top right corner. Two sets of shapes in each row are shaded black.
8	Three different sets of identical shapes therefore the missing picture has to feature triangles
9	Three different shapes with different shading
10	Three different shapes with different shading
11	In each column, the shapes in the squares on the left are the sum of the shapes in the other two squares.
12	In each column, the shapes in the squares on the left are the sum of the shapes in the other two squares.
13	In each column, the shape remains the same and the white square moves from the top to the middle to the bottom.
14	Each square has three squares with one black, two black and three black.
15	Three shapes, small, medium and large with different shading
16	In each column, three identical shapes with the shading in the outer, the middle, then the centre.
17	In each column, the middle parallelogram has the same outline and the pictures flip horizontally.
18	The nine squares create a tile pattern when complete.
19	The shapes in the left columns are a mirror image of the shapes in the boxes in the third column.
20	Three different patterns, small, medium and large with different shading
21	The shapes in the third columns are the shapes in the first two columns.

Extended answers
for Mixed Assessment Practice Paper A

Maths 1 p.27

1	400g × 3 = 1200g ÷ 6 = 200g
2	08:07 – 11 minutes = 07:56
3	£39.75 ÷ 5 = £7.95. £7.95 × 2 = £15.90
4	North – 90 degrees anticlockwise = west
5	$1 - \frac{1}{3} = \frac{2}{3}$. $\frac{1}{2}$ of $\frac{2}{3} = \frac{1}{3}$
6	09:20 + 2 hours 40 minutes = 12:00. 12:10 + 2 hours = 14:10
7	–2°C – 4°C = –6°C
8	$\frac{£3500}{17,500} = \frac{1}{5} = 20\%$
9	£3670 + £4122 = £7792. £12,000 – £7792 = £4208
10	20% = £25, therefore 100% = £25 × 5. £125
11	120% must equal 120%, therefore 100% equals 100g
12	Friday 31 August + 8 days = Saturday
13	525,948 rounded to the nearest hundred = 525,900
14	12:45 + 2 hours 45 minutes = 15:30
15	Capacity of coaches = 97 passengers. 6 + 30 + 42 = 78 leaving 19 spare seats
16	4 hours = 360° ÷ 3. 120°
17	£125 × 6 = £750
18	Probability = 3 in 45 (total number of children) or 1 in 15
19	£7.50 ÷ 2.5 must equal the cost of the sandwich (£3.00) therefore the crisps = £1.50
20	1 × £2 coin + 1 × £1 coin + 1 × 50p + 1 × 20p coin = £3.70
21	4.8kg – 1.2kg = 3.6kg. 3.6kg ÷ 12 = 300g

Maths 2 p.33

1	120ml × 5 = 600ml
2	168 miles × $\frac{2}{3}$ = 112 miles driven, therefore 56 miles left to drive
3	64 – 14 = 50. 50 ÷ 2 = 25, therefore Lily must have 25 goals, and Amalia 25 + 14 = 39
4	He must make 12 trips to carry 36 boxes + 1 extra trip with the remaining box
5	Sue = 40, Brian = 42, total age of parents = 82, leaving 26 for the children. Sasha = $2x$, Annie = x, Millie = $x + 2$. $4x + 2 = 26$, therefore $x = 6$. Sasha must be 12 years old.
6	Discount must be £400, therefore price of the car is £1600. £1600 ÷ £20 equals 80
7	Two layers equals 40 chocolates. 20% are milk chocolates therefore dark are 80%, 32
8	56 floors – 12 floors equals 44 floors
9	two fifths must be girls, one fifth of 90 equals 18, two fifths equals 36
10	Total doughnuts bought equals 60. Children eat 28 × 2 (56) plus 1 (teacher) = 57. Leaves 3.
11	£15 × 13 equals £195
12	One quarter of 156 equals 39

Blank page

CEM-style
11+ Mixed Assessment
Practice Paper B

Information about this practice paper:

- The time allowed is given at the start of each section.

- The page number appears at the bottom of each page.

- The title of each section is provided on the top line of each page.

- Answers should be clearly marked in pencil on the answer sheets on pages 66 and 67, in the spaces provided. Additional answer sheets are available at **https://shop.scholastic.co.uk/pass-your-11-plus/extras.**

- Use the pages of the test to write your workings out.

- If you make a mistake, rub it out and insert your new answer.

- If you are not sure of an answer, choose the one you think would be best; do not leave it blank.

 You will see this symbol at the beginning of each section. It will tell you how many minutes are allowed for that section.

Antonyms

Instructions

Select the word that has the OPPOSITE meaning to the word on the left.
Mark your answer on the answer sheet (page 66) by choosing one of the options A–E.
There is only one correct answer for each question.

Example 1

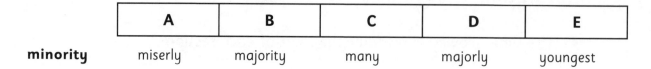

A	B	C	D	E

minority miserly majority many majorly youngest

The correct answer is:

B

majority

The answer, B, has been marked for you on the answer sheet.

Example 2

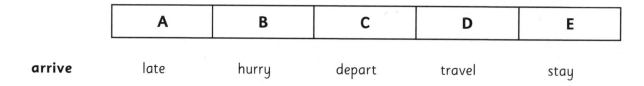

A	B	C	D	E

arrive late hurry depart travel stay

The correct answer is:

C

depart

Mark the box with the letter C on the answer sheet.

 You have 6 minutes for this section.

1		A	B	C	D	E
keen		uncaring	unwilling	undeserving	unloving	unsuspecting

2		A	B	C	D	E
deadly		careless	fearless	harmless	flawless	lifeless

3		A	B	C	D	E
kindle		astonish	cherish	distinguish	extinguish	garnish

4		A	B	C	D	E
honesty		deceit	debate	desire	demand	dispute

5		A	B	C	D	E
small		comfortable	authentic	modest	restricted	substantial

6		A	B	C	D	E
begin		eliminate	terminate	determine	commence	release

7		A	B	C	D	E
lessen		lose	squander	scatter	increase	compile

8 **heavy**

A	B	C	D	E
worthless	timeless	weightless	ruthless	pointless

9 **illuminate**

A	B	C	D	E
dampen	deafen	deepen	worsen	darken

10 **likely**

A	B	C	D	E
improbable	suspicious	unsatisfactory	believable	unwise

11 **otherwise**

A	B	C	D	E
additionally	likewise	moreover	including	without

12 **limited**

A	B	C	D	E
ageless	aimless	brief	changeable	endless

13 **calm**

A	B	C	D	E
humid	livid	lucid	rigid	timid

14 **repulsive**

A	B	C	D	E
adequate	standard	trendy	delightful	cheerful

	A	B	C	D	E
15 hurry	enter	loiter	pester	fluster	scatter

	A	B	C	D	E
16 found	dishevelled	unsettled	misplaced	disorganised	mistaken

	A	B	C	D	E
17 lucky	unfortunate	desperate	inappropriate	unhappy	joyous

	A	B	C	D	E
18 delicious	painful	mean	gruesome	revolting	spiteful

	A	B	C	D	E
19 sanity	joy	violence	disorder	irritation	madness

	A	B	C	D	E
20 rude	graceful	devoted	breezy	courteous	dignified

	A	B	C	D	E
21 manual	habitual	automatic	natural	intuitive	routine

22

few

A	B	C	D	E
less	scarce	numerous	regular	various

23

meeting

A	B	C	D	E
reunion	encounter	departure	parting	retirement

24

cruelty

A	B	C	D	E
luck	blessing	success	loyalty	mercy

25

separate

A	B	C	D	E
absorb	disperse	merge	admit	argue

26

huge

A	B	C	D	E
microscopic	significant	meaningful	graphic	amazing

Maths 3

Instructions

In this section you will be asked to mark your answers on the answer sheet (page 66) by choosing one of the options A–J shown at the top of each page.

A	B	C	D	E	F	G	H	I	J
72	75	56	60	28	52	26	48	80	90

Example 1

What is 14 + 38?

The answer is

F
52

The answer, F, has been marked for you on the answer sheet.

Example 2

What is 194 – 168

The answer is

G
26

Mark the box with the letter G on the answer sheet.

 You have **15** minutes for this section.

A	B	C	D	E	F	G	H	I	J
£25.00	£27.00	£42.00	£18.00	£67.50	£49.00	£21.00	£35.00	£40.00	£37.00

The children in Year 5 at Oak Park Primary School are all running 5 kilometres to raise money for charity.

1 Rosie completes her 5k run and raises £22.50 for her chosen charity.

Her friend Maya raises twice as much.

How much do the two friends raise altogether?

2 Jack, Thomas and Vikram raise funds for their charity in the ratio 4:2:3.

If Thomas raises £18, how much does Vikram raise?

3 Patrick and his best friend Ethan have a target of £50 that they would like to raise.

They manage to achieve 80% of their target.

How much do the two boys raise in total?

4 Hannah, Irena, Kieran and Hayden all manage to raise different amounts of money for their charity and the total amount that they manage to raise is £84.

What is the mean (average) amount that the four children raise?

A	B	C	D	E	F	G	H	I	J
2 hours	3 hours	5 hours	1 hour	2 hours	4 hours	1 hour	4 hours	4 hours	2 hours
30 mins	45 mins	25 mins	45 mins	25 mins	15 mins	35 mins	10 mins	45 mins	15 mins

Below is Zara's weekly school timetable.

Time	Monday	Tuesday	Wednesday	Thursday	Friday
09:00–09:15	Assembly	Assembly	Assembly	Assembly	Assembly
09:15–10:00	English	Maths	English	PSHE	English
10:00–11:00	Maths	English	Maths	English	History
Break					
11:20–12:00	RE	Music	History	ICT	Maths
12:00–12:45	Art	Topic	Science	Swimming	Maths
Lunch					
13:30–14:20	Geography	History	ICT	Music	RE
14:20–15:00	Topic	Science	Music	Art	French
15:00–15:30	Reading	PE	Gym	Geography	Reading

5 How much time will Zara be spending in English lessons each week?

_____

6 How many hours and minutes of maths lessons are there in Zara's weekly timetable?

_____

7 How much time will Zara spend doing some kind of sport?

_____

8 How much time will Zara spend having breaks and lunch?

A	B	C	D	E	F	G	H	I	J
18	16	240	6	5	225	36	210	27	7

There are a total of 360 passengers on board a flight from London to Dubai.

95% of the passengers are travelling economy class and the remaining passengers are all adults travelling in business class.

Three eighths of the passengers on board are children.

Economy tickets cost £260 each and business-class tickets cost £1300 each.

9 How many passengers are travelling in business class?

---

10 How many times more expensive than economy tickets are business-class tickets?

---

11 How many adults are there on the flight in total?

---

12 For every 40 passengers on the aircraft, there are three crew members.

How many crew members are there on the flight?

A	B	C	D	E	F	G	H	I	J
(3,7)	(3,5)	(4,1)	(7,3)	(5,3)	(3,2)	(1,4)	(2,3)	(8,2)	(7,2)

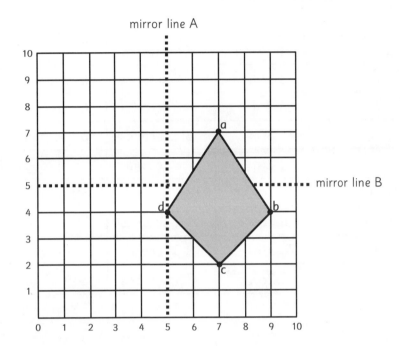

13 What would be the coordinates of point b if it were reflected in the mirror line A?

14 What would be the coordinates of point a if it were reflected in the mirror line A?

15 What would be the coordinates of point c if it were reflected in the mirror line A?

A	B	C	D	E	F	G	H	I	J
Bianca	Noah	Lucia	George	Olivia	Kieran	Priya	Ajay	Hannah	Zahid

Below is a table that shows some Year 5 results on sports day.

Pupil's name	High jump	100 metres	400 metres	Long jump
Bianca	73.5cm	17.2 seconds	62 seconds	2.98 metres
Noah	68.2cm	16.8 seconds	61 seconds	3.11 metres
Lucia	74.8cm	18.3 seconds	62 seconds	3.09 metres
George	72.2cm	17.8 seconds	59 seconds	2.76 metres
Olivia	76.7cm	18.1 seconds	58 seconds	2.46 metres
Kieran	78.2cm	16.2 seconds	55 seconds	3.21 metres
Priya	70.3cm	18.8 seconds	69 seconds	3.02 metres
Ajay	62.2cm	17.9 seconds	68 seconds	2.96 metres
Hannah	71.9cm	17.3 seconds	66 seconds	2.88 metres
Zahid	70.4cm	17.5 seconds	64 seconds	2.90 metres

16   Who won first prize for all four events?

_____

17   Who jumped exactly 10cm less than George in the high jump?

_____

18   Who was last in the 400 metres?

_____

19   Who was third in the high jump?

_____

20   Who jumped 15cm further than Ajay in the long jump?

Pictures 2

Instructions

Look at the sequence of pictures on the left.

Two pictures are missing and are shown by a question mark.

Pick two pictures from A–F on the right that best complete the sequence.

Mark your answers on the answer sheet (page 67) by choosing from the options A–F.

Examples 1 and 2

The answer to example 1 is D.

The answer, D, has been marked for you on the answer sheet.

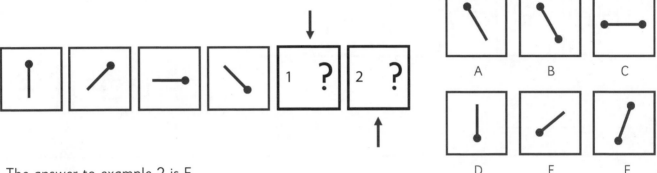

The answer to example 2 is E.

The answer E has been marked for you on the answer sheet.

Examples 3 and 4

The answer to example 3 is A.

Mark the box with the letter A on the answer sheet.

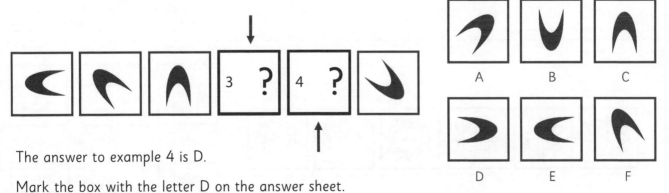

The answer to example 4 is D.

Mark the box with the letter D on the answer sheet.

You have 11 minutes for this section.

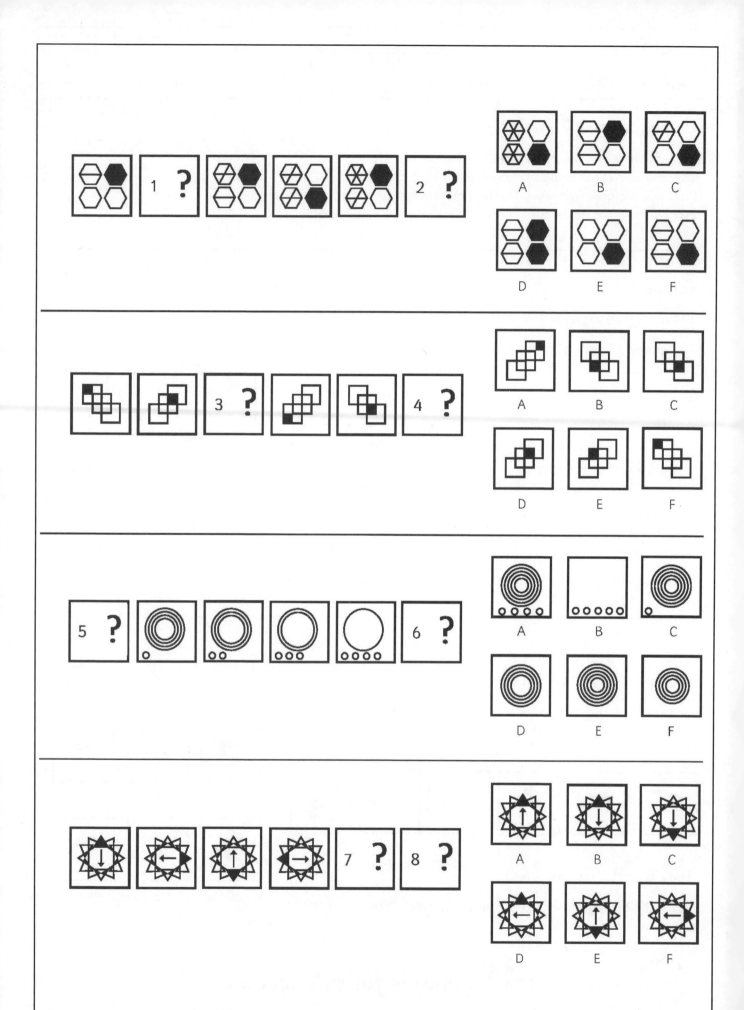

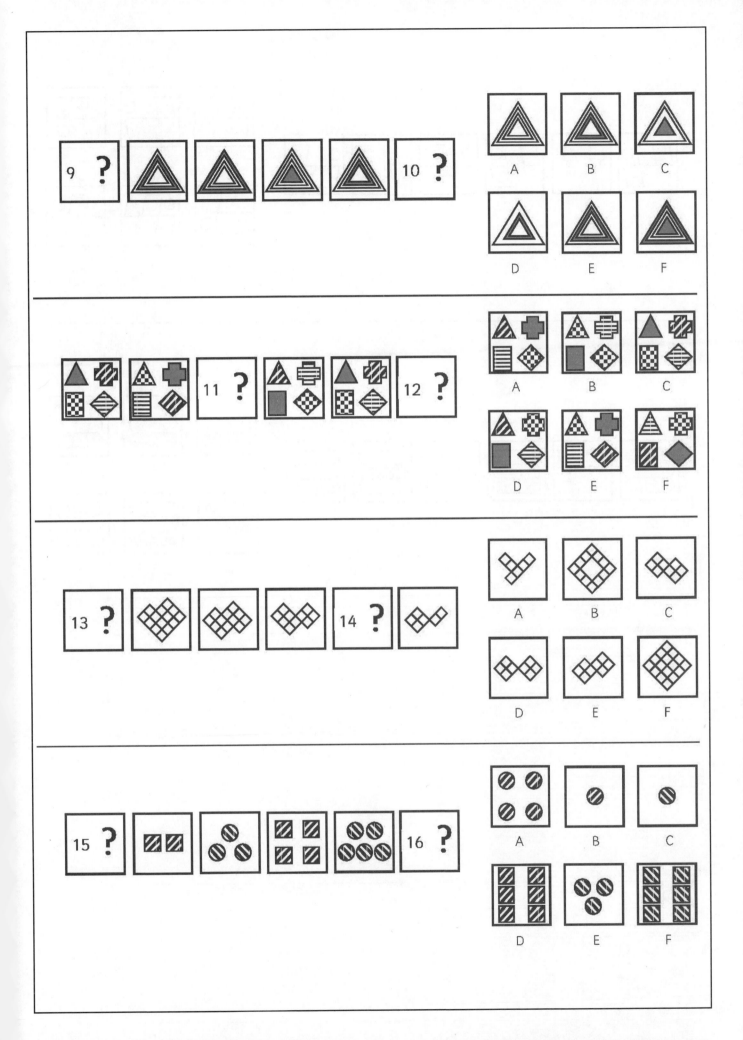

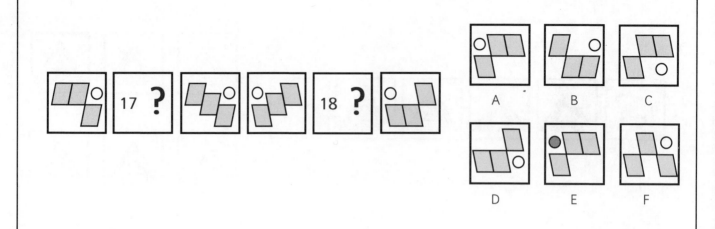

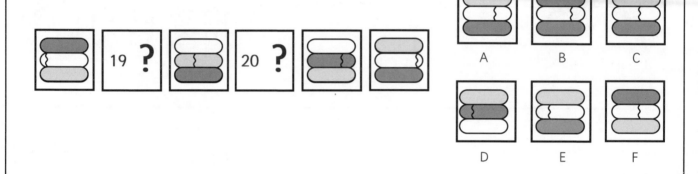

Cloze

Instructions

In the following passages, some of the words are missing. Please complete each passage by selecting the words from the options A–J. For each question, choose one word A–J and mark this on the answer sheet (page 67).

Each word can only be used once.

Example passage

A	B	C	D	E	F	G	H
glittered	majestic	ready	carved	throne	spun	adorn	sceptre

It was the night before the young 16-year-old prince was to be crowned king. He had gone to

bed early to rest, and lay there looking at all the things (Example **1**) for him to wear the next

morning. There was a robe of finely (Example **2**) gold, hand-stitched with beautiful patterns.

Example 1

The answer to example 1 is C, as the sentence should read:
It was the night before the young 16-year-old prince was to be crowned king. He had gone to bed early to rest, and lay there looking at all the things <u>ready</u> for him to wear the next morning.

The answer, C, has been marked for you on the answer sheet.

Example 2

The answer to example 2 is F, as the sentence should read:
There was a robe of finely <u>spun</u> gold, hand-stitched with beautiful patterns.

Mark the box with the letter F on the answer sheet.

 You have **7** minutes for this section.

Passage 1

A	B	C	D	E	F	G	H
flash	thought	intrigued	leafy	curved	skipped	reached	peculiar

There was a laurel-hedged walk which (Question **1**) round the secret garden and ended at a gate which opened into a wood, in the park. She (Question **2**) that she would enter through this gate and look into the wood and see if there were any rabbits about. She skipped along and when she (Question **3**) the little gate she opened it and went through because she heard a low, (Question **4**) sound and was (Question **5**) to find out what it was.

Passage 2

A	B	C	D	E	F	G	H
control	ripple	steady	sail	launched	ocean	paused	plunged

Having (Question **6**) our vessel, we attempted to embark. We sat astride the log, but found it was incredibly difficult to stop rolling round and being (Question **7**) into the water.

After half an hour's practice, we became expert enough to keep quite a (Question **8**) balance. As Jack and I kept watch, Peter laid down his paddle and baited his line with a whole oyster. He dropped it into deep water, and we all waited...

Our attention was suddenly attracted by a (Question **9**) on the surface, just a few yards away from us. Peter shouted to us to paddle in that direction because he thought it could be a large fish. Jack (Question **10**) and leaned forward towards the movement, before grabbing his paddle with both hands and barking, "Haul up your line, Peter! Seize your paddle, quick! It's a shark! it's a shark!"

Shuffled sentences

Instructions

Look at the examples. All the words form a sentence with one word left over. Select the word that does NOT belong in the sentence. Choose only one word for each sentence.

Mark your answer on the answer sheet (page 67) by choosing the letter, A–H, of the correct word.

Example 1

A	B	C	D	E	F	G	H
the	by	aeroplane	delayed	was	minutes	stopped	thirty

The sentence is:

D	C	E	D	B	H	F
the	aeroplane	was	delayed	by	thirty	minutes

So the leftover word is:

G
stopped

The answer, G, has been marked for you on the answer sheet.

Example 2

A	B	C	D	E	F	G	H
able	to	trainers	Yasmine	run	very	quickly	is

The sentence is:

D	H	A	B	E	F	G
Yasmine	is	able	to	run	very	quickly

So the left over word is:

C
trainers

Mark the box with the letter C on the answer sheet.

 You have 8 minutes for this section.

1

A	B	C	D	E	F	G	H
wanted	grow	tallest	Jakub	sunflower	to	planted	the

2

A	B	C	D	E	F	G	H
beautiful	Jenny	water	garden	in	likes	her	flowers

3

A	B	C	D	E	F	G	H
to	loves	chips	did	and	eat	Mabel	sausages

4

A	B	C	D	E	F	G	H
got	Kareem	his	locked	bedroom	accidentally	in	door

5

A	B	C	D	E	F	G	H
missed	by	minutes	ten	Rosie	train	her	from

6

A	B	C	D	E	F	G	H
in	stuck	an	some	album	Shawn	took	photographs

7

A	B	C	D	E	F	G	H
some	treated	to	Katya	bought	shoes	new	herself

8	A	B	C	D	E	F	G	H
	phone	time	photographs	some	his	Michael	on	took

9	A	B	C	D	E	F	G	H
	oven	the	Claire	in	some	took	cakes	baked

10	A	B	C	D	E	F	G	H
	late	home	school	Pavel	on	was	for	Friday

11	A	B	C	D	E	F	G	H
	hardly	no	there	the	in	were	fridge	vegetables

12	A	B	C	D	E	F	G	H
	stung	playing	nettle	Patrick	tennis	got	while	badly

13	A	B	C	D	E	F	G	H
	a	when	mouse	Annie	an	saw	she	screamed

14	A	B	C	D	E	F	G	H
	family	and	ordered	chips	the	plate	all	chicken

Answer sheets

Student name:

Antonyms p.46

Examples:

1   [A]   [B]   [C]   [D]   [E]
2   [A]   [B]   [C]   [D]   [E]

Questions

1   [A]   [B]   [C]   [D]   [E]
2   [A]   [B]   [C]   [D]   [E]
3   [A]   [B]   [C]   [D]   [E]
4   [A]   [B]   [C]   [D]   [E]
5   [A]   [B]   [C]   [D]   [E]
6   [A]   [B]   [C]   [D]   [E]
7   [A]   [B]   [C]   [D]   [E]
8   [A]   [B]   [C]   [D]   [E]
9   [A]   [B]   [C]   [D]   [E]
10   [A]   [B]   [C]   [D]   [E]
11   [A]   [B]   [C]   [D]   [E]
12   [A]   [B]   [C]   [D]   [E]
13   [A]   [B]   [C]   [D]   [E]
14   [A]   [B]   [C]   [D]   [E]
15   [A]   [B]   [C]   [D]   [E]
16   [A]   [B]   [C]   [D]   [E]
17   [A]   [B]   [C]   [D]   [E]
18   [A]   [B]   [C]   [D]   [E]
19   [A]   [B]   [C]   [D]   [E]
20   [A]   [B]   [C]   [D]   [E]
21   [A]   [B]   [C]   [D]   [E]
22   [A]   [B]   [C]   [D]   [E]
23   [A]   [B]   [C]   [D]   [E]
24   [A]   [B]   [C]   [D]   [E]
25   [A]   [B]   [C]   [D]   [E]
26   [A]   [B]   [C]   [D]   [E]

Maths 3 p.51

Examples:

1   [A]   [B]   [C]   [D]   [E]   [F]   [G]   [H]   [I]   [J]
2   [A]   [B]   [C]   [D]   [E]   [F]   [G]   [H]   [I]   [J]

Questions

1   [A]   [B]   [C]   [D]   [E]   [F]   [G]   [H]   [I]   [J]
2   [A]   [B]   [C]   [D]   [E]   [F]   [G]   [H]   [I]   [J]
3   [A]   [B]   [C]   [D]   [E]   [F]   [G]   [H]   [I]   [J]
4   [A]   [B]   [C]   [D]   [E]   [F]   [G]   [H]   [I]   [J]
5   [A]   [B]   [C]   [D]   [E]   [F]   [G]   [H]   [I]   [J]
6   [A]   [B]   [C]   [D]   [E]   [F]   [G]   [H]   [I]   [J]
7   [A]   [B]   [C]   [D]   [E]   [F]   [G]   [H]   [I]   [J]
8   [A]   [B]   [C]   [D]   [E]   [F]   [G]   [H]   [I]   [J]
9   [A]   [B]   [C]   [D]   [E]   [F]   [G]   [H]   [I]   [J]
10   [A]   [B]   [C]   [D]   [E]   [F]   [G]   [H]   [I]   [J]
11   [A]   [B]   [C]   [D]   [E]   [F]   [G]   [H]   [I]   [J]
12   [A]   [B]   [C]   [D]   [E]   [F]   [G]   [H]   [I]   [J]
13   [A]   [B]   [C]   [D]   [E]   [F]   [G]   [H]   [I]   [J]
14   [A]   [B]   [C]   [D]   [E]   [F]   [G]   [H]   [I]   [J]
15   [A]   [B]   [C]   [D]   [E]   [F]   [G]   [H]   [I]   [J]
16   [A]   [B]   [C]   [D]   [E]   [F]   [G]   [H]   [I]   [J]
17   [A]   [B]   [C]   [D]   [E]   [F]   [G]   [H]   [I]   [J]
18   [A]   [B]   [C]   [D]   [E]   [F]   [G]   [H]   [I]   [J]
19   [A]   [B]   [C]   [D]   [E]   [F]   [G]   [H]   [I]   [J]
20   [A]   [B]   [C]   [D]   [E]   [F]   [G]   [H]   [I]   [J]

Pictures 2 p.57 – Examples:

1	[A]	[B]	[C]	~~[D]~~	[E]	[F]
2	[A]	[B]	[C]	[D]	~~[E]~~	[F]
3	[A]	[B]	[C]	[D]	[E]	[F]
4	[A]	[B]	[C]	[D]	[E]	[F]

Questions

1	[A]	[B]	[C]	[D]	[E]	[F]
2	[A]	[B]	[C]	[D]	[E]	[F]
3	[A]	[B]	[C]	[D]	[E]	[F]
4	[A]	[B]	[C]	[D]	[E]	[F]
5	[A]	[B]	[C]	[D]	[E]	[F]
6	[A]	[B]	[C]	[D]	[E]	[F]
7	[A]	[B]	[C]	[D]	[E]	[F]
8	[A]	[B]	[C]	[D]	[E]	[F]
9	[A]	[B]	[C]	[D]	[E]	[F]
10	[A]	[B]	[C]	[D]	[E]	[F]
11	[A]	[B]	[C]	[D]	[E]	[F]
12	[A]	[B]	[C]	[D]	[E]	[F]
13	[A]	[B]	[C]	[D]	[E]	[F]
14	[A]	[B]	[C]	[D]	[E]	[F]
15	[A]	[B]	[C]	[D]	[E]	[F]
16	[A]	[B]	[C]	[D]	[E]	[F]
17	[A]	[B]	[C]	[D]	[E]	[F]
18	[A]	[B]	[C]	[D]	[E]	[F]
19	[A]	[B]	[C]	[D]	[E]	[F]
20	[A]	[B]	[C]	[D]	[E]	[F]

Cloze p.61 – Examples:

| 1 | [A] | [B] | ~~[C]~~ | [D] | [E] | [F] | [G] | [H] |
| 2 | [A] | [B] | [C] | [D] | [E] | [F] | [G] | [H] |

Questions

1	[A]	[B]	[C]	[D]	[E]	[F]	[G]	[H]
2	[A]	[B]	[C]	[D]	[E]	[F]	[G]	[H]
3	[A]	[B]	[C]	[D]	[E]	[F]	[G]	[H]
4	[A]	[B]	[C]	[D]	[E]	[F]	[G]	[H]
5	[A]	[B]	[C]	[D]	[E]	[F]	[G]	[H]
6	[A]	[B]	[C]	[D]	[E]	[F]	[G]	[H]
7	[A]	[B]	[C]	[D]	[E]	[F]	[G]	[H]
8	[A]	[B]	[C]	[D]	[E]	[F]	[G]	[H]
9	[A]	[B]	[C]	[D]	[E]	[F]	[G]	[H]
10	[A]	[B]	[C]	[D]	[E]	[F]	[G]	[H]

Shuffled sentences p.63 – Examples:

| 1 | [A] | [B] | [C] | [D] | [E] | [F] | ~~[G]~~ | [H] |
| 2 | [A] | [B] | [C] | [D] | [E] | [F] | [G] | [H] |

Questions

1	[A]	[B]	[C]	[D]	[E]	[F]	[G]	[H]
2	[A]	[B]	[C]	[D]	[E]	[F]	[G]	[H]
3	[A]	[B]	[C]	[D]	[E]	[F]	[G]	[H]
4	[A]	[B]	[C]	[D]	[E]	[F]	[G]	[H]
5	[A]	[B]	[C]	[D]	[E]	[F]	[G]	[H]
6	[A]	[B]	[C]	[D]	[E]	[F]	[G]	[H]
7	[A]	[B]	[C]	[D]	[E]	[F]	[G]	[H]
8	[A]	[B]	[C]	[D]	[E]	[F]	[G]	[H]
9	[A]	[B]	[C]	[D]	[E]	[F]	[G]	[H]
10	[A]	[B]	[C]	[D]	[E]	[F]	[G]	[H]
11	[A]	[B]	[C]	[D]	[E]	[F]	[G]	[H]
12	[A]	[B]	[C]	[D]	[E]	[F]	[G]	[H]
13	[A]	[B]	[C]	[D]	[E]	[F]	[G]	[H]
14	[A]	[B]	[C]	[D]	[E]	[F]	[G]	[H]

Answers

Antonyms
p.46

1	B
2	C
3	D
4	A
5	E
6	B
7	D
8	C
9	E
10	A
11	B
12	E
13	B
14	D
15	B
16	C
17	A
18	D
19	E
20	D
21	B
22	C
23	D
24	E
25	C
26	A

Maths 3
p.51

1	E
2	B
3	I
4	G
5	F
6	H
7	D
8	C
9	A
10	E
11	F
12	I
13	G
14	A
15	F
16	F
17	H
18	G
19	C
20	B

Pictures 2
p.57

1	F
2	A
3	C
4	D
5	E
6	B
7	B
8	F
9	B
10	E
11	F
12	E
13	F
14	D
15	C
16	D
17	A
18	B
19	D
20	F

Cloze
p.61

1	E
2	B
3	G
4	H
5	C
6	E
7	H
8	C
9	B
10	G

Shuffled
sentences p.63

1	G
2	C
3	D
4	H
5	H
6	G
7	E
8	B
9	F
10	B
11	A
12	C
13	E
14	F

Extended answers
for Mixed Assessment Practice Paper B

Antonyms p.46

1	keen means 'willing', therefore the antonym is 'unwilling'
2	deadly means 'harmful', therefore the antonym is 'harmless'
3	kindle means 'to set fire to', therefore the antonym is 'extinguish'
4	honesty means 'free from deceit', therefore the antonym is 'deceit'
5	small means 'little', therefore the antonym is 'substantial'
6	begin means 'to start', therefore the antonym is 'terminate'
7	lessen means 'to decrease', therefore the antonym is 'increase'
8	heavy means 'weighty', therefore the antonym is 'weightless'
9	illuminate means 'to light up', therefore the antonym is 'darken'
10	likely means 'probable', therefore the antonym is 'improbable'
11	otherwise means 'in a different way', therefore the antonym is 'likewise'
12	limited means 'within limits', therefore the antonym is 'endless'
13	calm means 'not angry', therefore the antonym is 'livid'
14	repulsive means 'nasty', therefore the antonym is 'delightful'
15	hurry means 'to go fast', therefore the antonym is 'loiter'
16	found means 'discovered', therefore the antonym is 'misplaced'
17	lucky means 'fortunate', therefore the antonym is 'unfortunate'
18	delicious means 'tasty', therefore the antonym is 'revolting'
19	sanity means 'common sense', therefore the antonym is 'madness'
20	rude means 'discourteous', therefore the antonym is 'courteous'
21	manual means 'operated by hand', therefore the antonym is 'automatic'
22	few means 'not very many', therefore the antonym is 'numerous'
23	meeting means 'coming together', therefore the antonym is 'parting'
24	cruelty means 'merciless', therefore the antonym is 'mercy'
25	separate means 'to disconnect', therefore the antonym is 'merge'
26	huge means 'very large', therefore the antonym is 'microscopic'

Extended answers
for Mixed Assessment Practice Paper B

Maths 3 p.51

1	£22.50 + £45.00 – £67.50
2	If Thomas raises £18, Vikram must raise half as much again which is £18 + £9
3	80% of £50 = £40
4	£84 ÷ by 4 equals £21
5	45 minutes x 3 = 135 minutes, plus 120 minutes = 255 minutes, which is 4 hours 15 minutes
6	45 minutes + 120 minutes + 40 minutes + 45 minutes = 4 hours 10 minutes
7	45 minutes + 30 minutes + 30 minutes = 1 hour 45 minutes
8	(20 minutes + 45 minutes) × 5 = 325 minutes or 5 hours 25 minutes
9	5% of 360 = 18
10	5 times – £1300 ÷ £260 = 5
11	Number of adults = five eighths of 360 which is 225
12	360 ÷ 40 = 9, therefore crew members will = 3 × 9
13	b would be 4 squares to the left of mirror line A – (1,4)
14	a would be 2 squares to the left of mirror line A – (3,7)
15	c would be 4 squares to the left of mirror line A – (3,2)
16	First prize was won by Kieran – it's only necessary to find his high jump score
17	10cm less than George would be 62.2cm – Ajay
18	Last in the 400 metres would be the longest time – Priya
19	3rd in the high jump would be the third highest measurement – 74.8cm – Lucia
20	15cm further than Ajay would be 296cm + 15cm = 311cm or 3.11m – Noah

Pictures 2 p.57

1 & 2	Top right hexagon alternates between top and bottom. A line is added to the hexagon in the bottom left each time.
3 & 4	The three squares are flipped horizontally each time and the small shaded square moves one.
5 & 6	The large circles lose one ring in each picture and gain a small circle.
7 & 8	The arrow in the centre of each picture rotates 90 degrees clockwise and the shaded triangle.
9 & 10	The shading in the triangles from the inside to the outside
11 & 12	Shapes all stay the same, the shading moves one space clockwise each time.
13 & 14	The pictures are losing two squares each time, alternating from the top to the bottom.
15 & 16	Alternating circles and squares and gaining one more shape with each picture.
17 & 18	The shapes are in pairs and are mirror images of each other.
19 & 20	The line in the middle shape is moving gradually to the right, shading is moving down.

Extended answers
for Mixed Assessment Practice Paper B

Cloze passage 1 p.61

There was a laurel-hedged walk which <u>curved</u> round the secret garden and ended at a gate which opened into a wood, in the park. She <u>thought</u> that she would enter through this gate and look into the wood and see if there were any rabbits about. She skipped along and when she <u>reached</u> the little gate she opened it and went through because she heard a low, <u>peculiar</u> sound and was <u>intrigued</u> to find out what it was.

Cloze passage 2 p.61

Having <u>launched</u> our vessel, we attempted to embark. We sat astride the log, but found it was incredibly difficult to stop rolling round and being <u>plunged</u> into the water.

After half an hour's practice, we became expert enough to keep quite a <u>steady</u> balance. As Jack and I kept watch, Peter laid down his paddle and baited his line with a whole oyster. He dropped it into deep water, and we all waited…

Our attention was suddenly attracted by a <u>ripple</u> on the surface, just a few yards away from us. Peter shouted to us to paddle in that direction because he thought it could be a large fish. Jack <u>paused</u> and leaned forward towards the movement, before grabbing his paddle with both hands and barking, "Haul up your line, Peter! Seize your paddle, quick! It's a shark! it's a shark!"

Shuffled sentences p.63

1	Jakub wanted to grow the tallest sunflower
2	Jenny likes beautiful flowers in her garden
3	Mabel loves to eat sausages and chips
4	Kareem accidentally got locked in his bedroom
5	Rosie missed her train by ten minutes
6	Shawn stuck some photographs in an album
7	Katya treated herself to some new shoes
8	Michael took some photographs on his phone
9	Claire baked some cakes in the oven
10	Pavel was late for school on Friday
11	There were no vegetables in the fridge
12	Patrick got badly stung while playing tennis
13	Annie screamed when she saw a mouse
14	The family all ordered chicken and chips